My Second
Handwriting Activity Book

My name is _____

Letterland fairground

Write over the letters and add some more to finish the fairground scene.

The letters **c**, **o**, **a**, **d**, **g** and **q** all start with the same circular handwriting movement. Point out the curved arrows. Explain that the dot is the starting point and then the arrow should be followed.

queue here

Putting up posters

Help the Letterlanders to fill up their posters by going over their letters and adding some more.

lifeboat

Impy's ink machine

Help Impy Ink and Uppy Umbrella by writing in their letter shapes.

Point out that Impy Ink's dot should come after writing his letter. Writing the **u** shape provides a useful warm up for writing the letter **y**.

Juggling jellies

Fill up these delicious jellies with Jumping Jim's letter and Yo-yo Man's letter.

PARENT POINTER

Point out that the down stroke for the Yo-yo Man's letter and for Jumping Jim's letter goes through the line. Remind your child not to forget Jumping Jim's 'ball' (the dot) over his letter.

Fun and games

Write these Letterlanders' letters on their play things for them.

Poor Peter's Pillow

These letters - **h**, **b** and **p** - provide good practice in making a strong downward stroke, then a curve. It is important to notice where each letter meets the line.

Read all about it

These three Letterlanders have letters that all start the same way. Can you fill them in?

Because **n**, **r** and **m** use similar strokes, together they help your child's hand to learn the habit of forming all their shapes correctly.

PARENT POINTER

9

Flying high

Fill in these letters up in the air! Except for Eddy Elephant's letter, they are all made with straight lines.

Remind your child to begin Eddy Elephant's letter with a straight line before curving 'around his head'. All the straight letters provide practice in controlled short, sharp hand movements.

PARENT POINTER

10

Capital letters

Help all the Letterlanders to fill in their capital letters. Remember to start at the top each time!

PARENT POINTER

The next four pages give your child plenty of practice in writing capital letters. Explain that capital letters are mostly used for starting important words like people's names, and for starting sentences.

First words

Now you can start writing whole words!
Write over the dotted words and then try writing
them by yourself.

an acrobat

big bubbles

catch a cold

d e f

doll's dress

eleven eggs

fat frog

17

g h i

good game

happy horse

invite him in

j k l

jam jars

keep the kitten

long letter

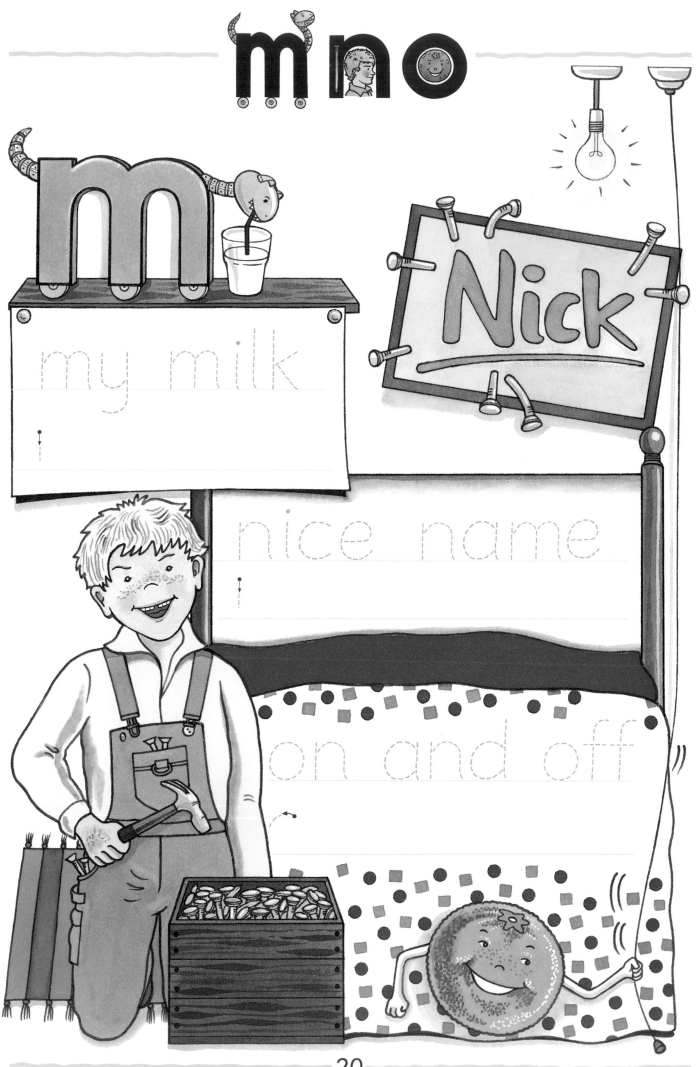

m n o

my milk

Nick

nice name

on and off

p q r

pink pig

quick quiz

red rug

s t u v

soft snow

two trees

under the van

w x y z

windy weather

six yo-yos

lazy zebra

Days of the week

Write over these days of the week.

Monday

Tuesday

Wednesday

Thursday

Friday

Saturday

Sunday